WITH
PIANO ACCOMPANIMENT.

FLUTE FANCIES.

COMPILED & ARRANGED BY
Hugh M. Stuart.

CONTENTS

BOSTON MUSIC COMPANY.

4.50

FOREWORD

This is a collection of graded flute solos aimed at developing musicianship in the young player. It includes music ranging from the Baroque period to the Modern period, selected on the basis of its adaptability to the flute and its appeal to the young student.

Since the development of fine tone quality and absolute control of the breath stream are essential to good flute playing, ample material which will help develop these skills is included.

As a further aid, the breathing has been carefully marked. Breath marks in parentheses (') are for temporary use only and should be abandoned as the student progresses.

Interpretative notes and dynamic markings have been included to help develop musicianship.

It it my hope that students using this collection will learn that there is more to flute study than merely playing the correct notes and rhythms. A sensitive feeling for the music itself should be the prime consideration.

H.M.S.

Allegretto

A. Diabelli

Minuet

I. Pleyel

Rigaudon

H. Purcell

Berceuse

M. Hauser

Little Piece

R. Schumann

Arietta

E. Grieg

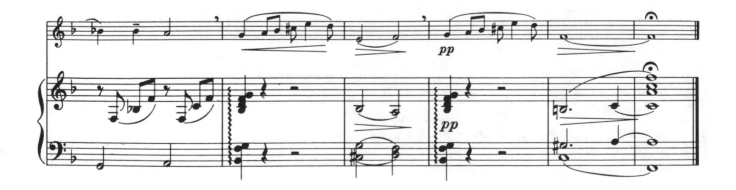

Air

L. van Beethoven

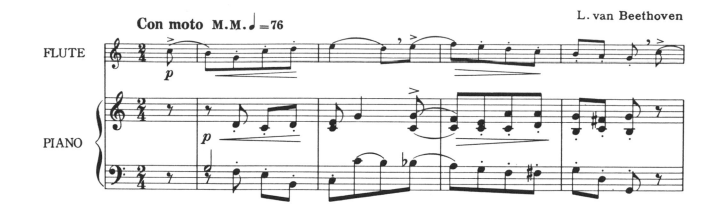

Sonata Theme

W. A. Mozart

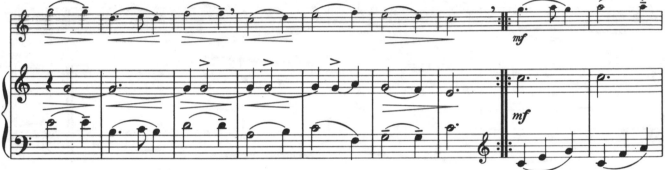

Musette

J. S. Bach

Minuetto

W. A. Mozart

Dance

F. Schubert

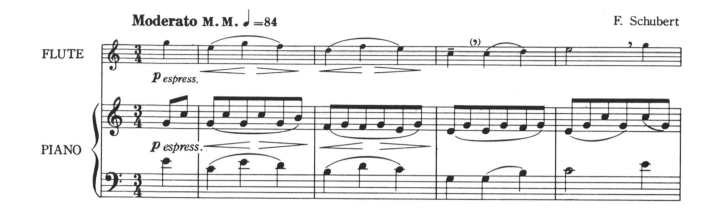

Waltz

F. Schubert

Andante Op. 29

F. Schubert

Prelude
Op. 28 No. 4

F. Chopin

Ecossaise

L. van Beethoven

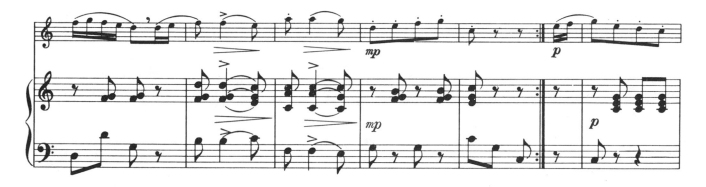

Siciliana

A. Scarlatti

Allegro

W. A. Mozart

Greensleeves

Old English

Song

Moderato M. M. ♩=54

R. Schumann

Air

Gottlieb Muffat

Cats
The fabulous hit musical by Andrew Lloyd Webber. Based on 'Old Possum's Book of Practical Cats' by T.S. Eliot. All the songs arranged for piano with lyrics and chord symbols.
(BCD), AM 31006

Walt Disney Vocal Selections: Cinderella
Arranged for piano, with lyrics and chord symbols.
(B), WD 10039

The Jungle Book
Vocal selection arranged for piano/vocal, with guitar chord symbols.
(ABC), WD 10013

Evita
Musical excerpts and libretto.
(CD), EVM 10005

Fiddler On The Roof
Vocal selections from the show. 11 numbers including 'If I Were A Rich Man' and 'Sunrise, Sunset'.
(D), AM 39520

Jesus Christ Superstar
Musical excerpts and complete libretto.
(CD), LE 11110

The New Illustrated Disney Songbook
Seventy-three memorable Disney songs from such favourite films as 'Snow White and the Seven Dwarfs', 'Pinocchio', 'Cinderella', 'The Jungle Book' and many more. Arranged for piano/vocal with guitar boxes. Full colour illustrations.
(CD), OP44031

Walt Disney's Bambi Songbook
All the songs from the film. Arranged for piano/vocal with chord boxes. Colour illustrations.
(AB), CC11321

Smike
Libretto *(B), AV 51860*
Vocal Score *(B), AV 51878*

The Walt Disney Songbook
Walt Disney favourites from 'Davy Crockett', 'The Jungle Book', 'Bedknobs And Broomsticks', 'Cinderella', 'Mary Poppins', 'The Happiest Millionaire', 'Pinocchio', 'Snow White' and other shows. 25 numbers for piano with lyrics and chord symbols.
(C), AM19316

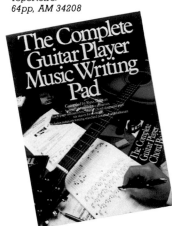

The Complete Guitar Player Music Writing Book
The only music writing book specially compiled for guitarists. Enables you to keep a complete record of your own songs and repertoire.
64pp, AM 34208

The Complete Guitar Player Music Writing Pad
Sixty-four pages, each containing ten blank chord diagrams and 6 staves for notation.
64pp, AM 34216

Woodstock Music Manuscript Paper
A4, 12 stave, *32pp, WO 10166*
A4, 12 stave, spiral, *32pp, WO 10174*
A5L, 6 stave, spiral *32pp, WO 10224*
A5L, 6 stave stitched, *32pp, WO 10216*
A4, 12 stave, punched, *48pp, WO 10182*
A4, 12 stave, *64pp, WO 10190*
A4, 12 stave, spiral, *64pp, WO 10208*

The Complete Guitar Player Video
with Russ Shipton
Full colour teaching video lasting 60 minutes which is an important addition to The Complete Guitar Player series. A self-contained home study course.
VHS *(CD), OV 10002*
Beta *(CD), OV 10010*

How To Read Music
with Frederick Noad
Even if you have never read a note of music, this 51-minute, full-colour video will teach you how. Ideal for classroom or private teaching.
VHS *(CD), OV 10028*
Beta *(CD), OV 10093*

Jigsaw
Popular tunes for school orchestras. This series of flexible arrangements may be used with players of wide ranging abilities. Pack includes Conductor Score and parts for instruments including piano, recorder, violin, euphonium, cello, flute, bass, oboe and trumpet etc.
EastEnders (BC), AM65798
I Know Him So Well (BC), AM66747

We Wish You A Merry Christmas
by Barrie Carson Turner
Five variations scored for classroom ensemble and piano. This pack includes: piano/conductor score, 6 recorder and 4 each tuned and untuned percussion parts.
(BC), AM65202

Clarinet

Beatles, Themes And Variations: Clarinet
Seven Beatles themes with three variations. Pull-out piano accompaniment. Also for flute and trumpet.
(I), NO 17873

Graded Solos For Clarinet
Forty popular songs selected and arranged by Robin de Smet. Also for flute and trumpet.
(EI), AM 33598

Lennon & McCartney For Clarinet
This book presents over fifty compositions arranged for the clarinet. Also for trumpet and flute.
(I), NO 17725

100 Solos: Clarinet
Graded solos for players of all standards. Each piece is complete in itself and requires no piano accompaniment. Also for flute, saxophone, trumpet and violin.
(EI), AM 33689

101 Popular Songs For Trumpet And Clarinet
Arranged in solo and duet form. A collection of popular and traditional tunes.
(EI), HS 10445

The Complete Clarinet Player
by Paul Harvey
Based on popular songs and light classics. Clear text, diagrams, photographs.
Book 1
Blow your first notes and learn the rudiments of music. Play songs such as 'Love Me Tender', 'Yellow Submarine' . . . Fingering chart.
(CD), AM62613
Book 2 (CD), AM62621
Book 3 (CD), AM62639
Book 4 (CD), AM62647

Associated Board Examination Grades
(E) Elementary – Grades 1-3
(I) Intermediate – Grades 4-6
(Ad) Advanced – Grades 6-8
(T) Teacher's Book

Flute

Beatles, Themes And Variations: Flute
Seven Beatles themes with three variations. Pull-out piano accompaniment. Also for clarinet and trumpet.
(I), NO 17865

50 Selected Children's Classics
Includes 'Arabesque', 'Barcarolle' and 'Canon in D'. Also for recorder and piano.
(E), HS 10551

Flute Solos (EFS 38)
Effective arrangements of over 50 pieces. The wide range of compositions includes works of Beethoven, Brahms, Dvořák, Schubert and many others as well as folk songs, dances' jigs and reels from all over the world. Each piece includes piano accompaniment.
(BCD), AM 40197

Graded Solos For Flute
Forty popular songs selected and arranged by Robin de Smet. Also for clarinet and trumpet.
(BD), AM 33812

Lennon & McCartney For Flute
This book presents over fifty compositions arranged for the flute. Also for trumpet and clarinet.
(I), NO 17717

100 Solos: Flute
Graded solos for players of all standards. Each piece is complete and does not require piano accompaniment. Also for clarinet, saxophone, trumpet and violin.
(EI), AM 33812

One Hundred And One Solos For The Flute
An outstanding collection of popular and light classical music arranged by Robin De Smet. Includes 'Chanson Triste', 'EastEnders' and 'The Power Of Love'.
(CD), AM63538

Selected Flute Solos (EFS 101)
This volume contains a group of the finest standard flute solos selected for their diversity in style and suitability for concert and contest use. Among the selections are works by Pessard, Chaminade, Mozart, Handel, Mendelssohn, Gluck, Fauré and Godard. All have piano accompaniment.
(Ad), AM 40403

The Complete Flute Player
by John Sands
The only flute course using popular tunes. Clear text, photographs and diagrams.
Book 1
Assembling the flute and producing your first sounds. Left hand notes, music notation and 7 keys. Music by Lennon & McCartney and John Denver etc.
(CD), AM62852
Book 2 (CD), AM62860
Book 3 (CD), AM62878
Book 4 (CD), AM62886

Penny Whistle

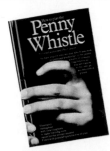

How To Play The Penny Whistle
by Gina Landor & Phil Cleaver
No previous knowledge required. Illustrated with clear diagrams. Also contains many popular tunes to play.
(E), AM 27137

The Penny Whistle Book
by Robin Williamson
A complete guide to the penny whistle for beginning to advanced players using a new systematic approach to fingering. Contains information on modal playing and 56 penny whistle tunes. Superb as a beginner's text, also of great use to the advanced player.
(EIAd), OK 63271

Abba Songs For The Recorder
A selection of favourite Abba songs specially arranged for the recorder. Published complete with lyrics and guitar diagrams plus a two-page introduction to playing the recorder. Includes 'Waterloo' and 'Knowing Me, Knowing You'.
(I), AM 19720

Appalachian Folk Songs For Recorder
by Ralph Wm. Zeitlin
Thirty traditional folk songs and tunes arranged as solos and duets for soprano and alto recorders.
(I), AM 35650

Around The World With My Recorder
by Harry Dexter
Includes 101 selected song favourites in easy to play recorder arrangements.
(E), HS 11542

Bach For Recorder
by Cliff Tobey
Solos and duets arranged for soprano and tenor recorders.
(IAd), AY 15406

Baroque & Folk Tunes For The Recorder
An unusual collection of music arranged for the recorder – fifty pieces from over 300 years of music.
(I), AM 17948

Beatles For Recorder
Easy new arrangements by Robin de Smet, of famous Beatles songs. Thirty tunes with chord symbols.
(E), AM 18434

Beatles Songs For The Recorder
Outstanding collection of Beatles songs arranged specially for recorder. Complete with lyrics and guitar diagrams. Includes a two-page introduction to playing the recorder.
(I), NO 17394

Children's Songs For The Recorder
Twenty-five songs especially arranged for recorder with lyrics and guitar chord boxes.
(I), AM 13673

Christmas Songs For The Recorder
Over 20 of the best known Christmas carols arranged for recorder with lyrics and guitar boxes.
(E), AM 20157

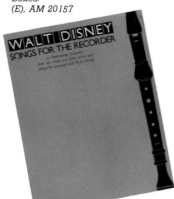

Walt Disney Songs For The Recorder
Twenty-five outstanding selections from the shows and films which will always be associated with Walt Disney. Includes lyrics and guitar boxes.
(I), WD 10070

Early Music For Recorder
arranged by Robin de Smet
Easy new arrangements of airs and dances from the 10th to the 16th century. 47 tunes with chord symbols.
(E), AM 36542

Elizabethan Music For Recorder
by Ralph Wm. Zeitlin
Solos, duets, trios and rounds arranged for soprano, alto and tenor recorders.
(I), AY 15315

50 Selected Children's Classics
Includes 'Arabesque', 'Barcarolle', 'Canon in D'. Also for flute and piano.
(E), HS 10569

50 Songs For Recorder Book 1
For recorder with guitar accompaniment. Includes 'California Dreaming', 'Fernando' and 'Bright Eyes'.
(I), AM 29885

50 Songs For Recorder Book 2
For recorder and guitar accompaniment. Includes 'Top of the World', 'Little Buttercup' and 'Sailing'.
(I), AM 29893

Film Music For The Recorder
Twenty-eight well known film titles arranged for recorder, with lyrics and guitar boxes.
(I), AM 25701

Film And TV Themes For The Recorder
Over 20 notable tunes used as film and TV themes with lyrics and guitar chord boxes.
(I), AM 13962

Folk Songs For The Recorder
Twenty-seven famous folk songs arranged for recorder, with lyrics and guitar boxes.
(I), AM 29000

How To Play The Recorder
Pocket size recorder tutor which is a complete course for the beginner that is easy and fun to play.
(E), AM 35551

Hymns For Recorder
Easy new arrangements by Robin de Smet of 34 best loved hymn tunes. With chord symbols and words.
(E), AM 36559

Irish Music For Recorder
New easy arrangements by Robin de Smet of famous Irish songs and melodies. 30 tunes with chord symbols.
(E), AM 36534

Jazz For The Recorder
A contrasting selection of popular and jazz standards. Includes lyrics and guitar chord boxes.
(I), AM 28994

Paul McCartney: Songs for the Recorder
Twenty-seven songs including 'Mull of Kintyre', 'My Love'. With lyrics and guitar diagrams plus a 2-page introduction to playing the recorder.
(I), MY 70358

My Very First Recorder Songbook. Book A
Fifteen easy to play songs, folk tunes and songs from shows and films. With piano accompaniment and separate recorder part.
(E), AM 34158
Book B
(E), AM 34166

New Popular Songs For The Recorder
Published complete with lyrics and guitar chord boxes.
(E), AM 31501

Oliver: Songs For The Recorder
Outstanding selection from the show, with lyrics and guitar chord boxes, plus a six-page introduction to playing the recorder.
(I), AM 13368

Paul Simon Songs For The Recorder
Twenty songs including lyrics and guitar diagrams plus a two-page introduction to playing the recorder.
(I), PS 10016

Songs And Dances Of England
An outstanding collection of songs and dances from England's musical heritage. Arranged for voice and recorder, penny whistle or flute, or other suitable 'C' instruments.
(EI), AM 31428

Songs And Dances Of Ireland
A collection of songs from Ireland's rich musical heritage. All arranged for voice and recorder, penny whistle or flute, or other suitable 'C' instrument.
(EI), AM 31402

Songs And Dances Of Scotland
An exciting collection of songs and dances all arranged for voice and recorder, flute, penny whistle or other 'C' instrument. With chord symbols and guitar diagrams, plus full lyrics.
(EI), AM 31410

Cat Stevens Songs For The Recorder
Complete with lyrics and guitar boxes. Plus a two page introduction to playing the recorder.
(I), AM 23425

10 Famous Pop Songs For Recorder
For solos or ensemble playing. Piano accompaniment available. Can be played with any other instrument in the series. Includes 'Michelle' and 'Unforgettable'. Lyrics and chord symbols. Also for violin, saxophone, flute, clarinet and trumpet.
(E), AM 28614

Piano Accompaniments
(E), AM 28507

Together For Two Recorders And Guitar
A variety of music ranging from Purcell to Pop. Mozart's 'Allegro' is joined by melodies such as 'Clementine' and 'Rivers Of Babylon'. With lyrics, chord symbols and guitar boxes.
Book 1 *(E), AM 29901*

Together For Two Recorders And Guitar
For C Recorders and guitars playing in ensemble. Boccherini's 'Minuet' to 'Yesterday'. Lyrics, chord symbols, and guitar boxes.
Book 2 *(E), AM 29919*

Associated Board Examination Grades
(E) Elementary – Grades 1-3
(I) Intermediate – Grades 4-6
(Ad) Advanced – Grades 6-8
(T) Teacher's Book

Continued . . .

Saxophone

101 Easy Sax Solos & Duets
A collection of popular and traditional tunes.
(E), HS 11864

100 Solos: Saxophone
Graded solos for players of all standards. Each piece is complete in itself and requires no piano accompaniment. Also for clarinet, flute, recorder, trumpet and violin.
(EI), AM 33697

The Complete Saxophone Player
by Raphael Ravenscroft
This course is based on popular tunes and light classics. With clear text, diagrams and photographs it will prove easy to understand even to those with no knowledge of music.
Book 1 (CD), AM62712
Book 2 (CD), AM62720
Book 3 (CD), AM62738
Book 4 (CD), AM62746

Trumpet

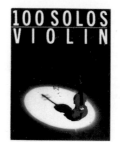

The Complete Trumpet Player
by Don Bateman
Based on popular songs and light classics. Clear text, diagrams, photographs.
Book 1
Rudiments of music, technique, the notes Low G to High D. Play songs such as 'I'd Like To Teach The World To Sing' and 'Edelweiss'.
(CD), AM39207
Book 2 (CD), AM39215
Book 3 (CD), AM39223
Book 4 (CD), AM39231

101 Solos For The Trumpet
arranged by Robin De Smet
An outstanding collection of music for trumpet covering a wide range of popular and light classical music.
(CD), AM61870

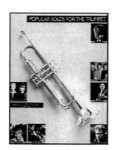

Popular Solos For The Trumpet
Over 30 hits from today's top artists. Includes 'Caribbean Queen', 'Walk Of Life', 'We Don't Need Another Hero' and 'When The Going Gets Tough'. No piano accompaniment required.
(CD), AM63108

Violin

100 Solos For Violin
Graded solos for players of all standards. The pieces are complete in themselves and require no piano accompaniment. Includes 'Dancing Queen', 'Michelle' and 'English Country Garden'.
(CD), AM33671

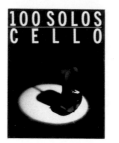

100 Cello Solos
Graded solos for players of all standards. The pieces are complete in themselves and require no accompaniment.
(CD), AM63231

Cello Solos
Easy to intermediate arrangements designed to bring out the finest qualities of the cello.
(CD), AM64486

Christmas Solos

Christmas Solos For The Clarinet
arranged by Robin De Smet
A unique collection of 49 traditional and up-to-date Christmas songs including 'Santa Claus Is Comin' To Town', 'When Santa Got Stuck Up The Chimney', 'Winter Wonderland' and many more. With chord symbols.
(CD), AM65020

Christmas Solos For The Flute
arranged by Robin De Smet
A unique collection of 53 traditional and up-to-date Christmas songs including 'Frosty The Snowman', 'I Believe In Father Christmas', 'Santa Claus Is Comin' To Town'. With chord symbols.
(CD), AM65038

Christmas Solos For The Recorder
arranged by Robin De Smet
A unique collection of 50 traditional and up-to-date Christmas songs including 'Away In A Manger', 'Silent Night', 'Santa Claus Is Comin' To Town' and 'Winter Wonderland'.
(CD), AM65046

Christmas Solos For The Bb Saxophone
arranged by Robin De Smet
A unique collection of more than 50 traditional and up-to-date Christmas songs including 'The First Nowell', 'Santa Claus Is Comin' To Town', 'Silent Night' and 'Winter Wonderland'. With chord symbols.
(CD), AM65061

Christmas Solos For The Trumpet
arranged by Robin De Smet
A unique collection of 49 traditional and up-to-date Christmas songs including 'Santa Claus Is Comin' To Town', 'When Santa Got Stuck Up The Chimney', 'Winter Wonderland' and many more. With chord symbols.
(CD), AM65053

Christmas Solos For The Violin
Standard carols and songs for the festive season arranged for the beginning-to-intermediate player. Chord symbols facilitate optional piano or guitar accompaniment.
(CD), AM67133

All books in this catalogue are available from your local music dealer. In case of difficulty contact:
Music Sales Limited
Newmarket Road, Bury St Edmunds IP33 3YB.

Romance

L. van Beethoven

Ländler

F. Schubert

Poem

Z. Fibich

Bourrée

G. F. Handel

Allegro M. M. ♩=60

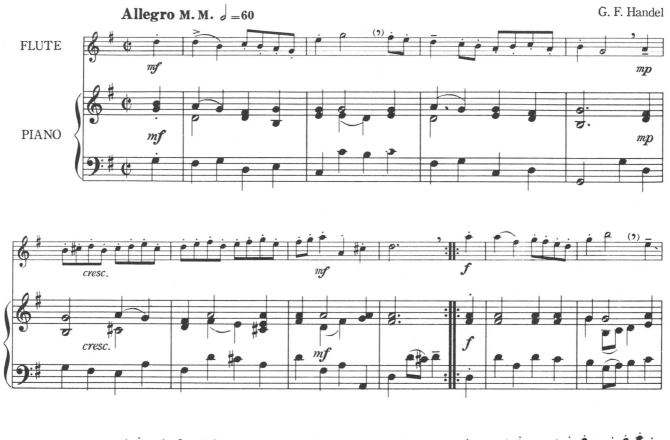

To A Wild Rose

E. MacDowell

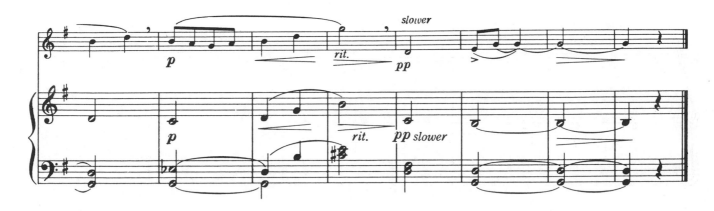

Etude Op.10, No 3

F. Chopin

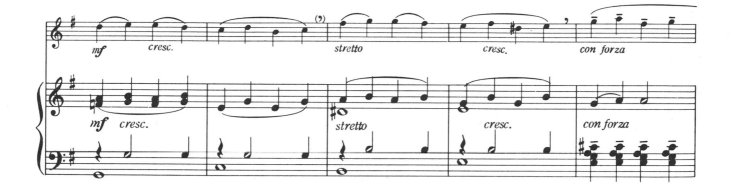

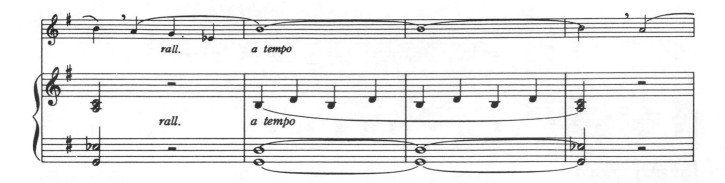

Gavotte
(Mignon)

A. Thomas

Gavotte

Allgro piu moderato M.M. ♩=60

J. S. Bach

Minuet

G. Bizet

Theme From Scheherazade

N Rimsky-Korsakoff

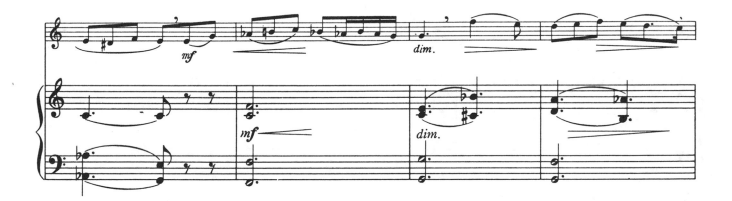

Sonata Theme
（Op.120 No,1）

J. Brahms

Allegro M. M. ♩=152

Lento and Andante
(Ballet Suite No.2)

C. W. von Gluck

Printed in England by Commercial Colour Press, 6/91(12036)